A *Selection* of
Italian Arias

c.1600 – *c*.1800

Low Voice • Volume II

Edition prepared by Damian Cranmer
English translations by Dorothy Richardson
Edition supervised by Michael Pilkington

The Associated Board of
the Royal Schools of Music

Contents

Preface

This volume contains several Italian songs and arias, most of which are well known from 19th-century editions. The strength of the vocal line in the music of this period, allied to a natural simplicity, makes this repertoire ideal material for the development of the young voice as well as providing excellent concert music.

Most of the pieces have been re-edited from contemporary sources. Two, *Pietà, Signore* attributed to Stradella and Caldara's *Come raggio di sol*, are found only in later sources; their accompaniments are piano parts and not realizations. Another exception, *Se tu m'ami* attributed to Pergolesi (but probably by Parisotti), exists only in 19th-century sources and again has a piano accompaniment. A case could be made for excluding it from a volume that attempts to present classical material in authentic form, but it has become so closely associated with this musical type that it has been included to avoid disappointment. An attempt to reconstruct it in 18th-century style was quickly abandoned and it is presented here in its customary form. The search for earlier sources produced an alternative setting of *Se tu m'ami*, possibly by Paolo Rolli, which has found a place in the selection.

The sources for the remaining pieces contain just a melody and a bass line, though some have string ritornelli, which are indicated by brackets over the top line when the string passages are intermittent. The added accompaniments have been kept simple and will be sufficient for most occasions, but pianists should feel free to adapt them as circumstances dictate. Left-hand octaves should be avoided, but there are a few passages where the left hand should be played an octave lower in order to avoid a melody sung by a broken male voice descending below the bass line. Some of the realizations of the accompaniments were begun by Philip Cranmer.

Suggestions for ornamentation have been included and it is hoped that singers will be encouraged to experiment with their own ideas. To a singer who asks if he or she has to do the ornamentation, the simple answer is yes: it is never too soon to learn the art of embellishment. It should be borne in mind that ornamentation is a structural device designed to emphasize the shape of a piece. The embellishment should be more adventurous towards the end of a section: there is no point in introducing a reprise with a great flourish and then singing the rest of the repeat exactly as the first time. The Rolli version of *Se tu m'ami* has been set with alternate verses ornamented, though even this arrangement needs consideration. One solution would be to sing the repeats in verses 1 and 7 only, thereby avoiding repetition of any ornamentation. There are simpler approaches (such as reducing the number of verses) and also more adventurous ones, given a singer's willingness to experiment with a personal creative style.

Regarding the English singing translations, it is obviously preferable to sing these pieces in the original language and all singers should be encouraged to develop their understanding of the Italian language. But there will be occasions when the English version is appropriate and these new translations can be sung confidently and without apology.

My thanks are due to Leslie East and Caroline Perkins of ABRSM Publishing for bringing to fruition a project that began some years ago when Martin Teale researched the sources for pieces selected by Marjorie Thomas and Gordon Clinton; to Michael Pilkington for additional material and a very significant contribution in preparing the musical text for engraving and printing; to Dorothy Richardson for her painstaking efforts to create English singing translations for the songs; and to the libraries, mentioned on pp. 79–80, for supplying copies of manuscripts and early printed editions in their possession.

Damian Cranmer

Notes on this edition

This volume of Italian arias uses the earliest available sources, which are listed on pp. 79–80. The voice part follows these sources with some modifications. The Italian has been modernized, as have key signatures and time signatures. Where a key signature has been modernized this is stated in a footnote, but only for songs printed in the original key. Where the original barring is irregular, additional dotted bar-lines have been supplied. Missing accidentals are shown in small print and redundant ones have been omitted. Some editorial slurs – shown with a stroke through them – have been added for consistency. Slurs have been included with the suggestions for ornamentation to clarify the underlay of text (dotted slurs have been used for the English text). As the sources rarely provide dynamic markings, and only occasionally tempo indications, suggestions for both are given in square brackets. Hemiolas are indicated by editorial brackets above the stave. For ease of reading, repeats have been written out in some of the pieces. Note that beaming follows the primary source.

In the accompaniment, the bass line also follows the sources. The few songs that have a full figured-bass give the figures as shown in the sources; when the song is transposed accidentals are adjusted to fit the new key. Note, however, that ♭5 indicates a diminished 5th regardless of key. Instrumental parts in the sources have been transcribed as they stand, which means that when transposed the result may well be out of range of the original instrumentation. To be playable on the keyboard, these passages may also require some modification. Such adjustments have been left to the judgement of the individual performer. Some additional notes – shown in small print – have been added by Damian Cranmer to complete the harmony. The continuo realizations are also by him.

Of the individual arias, the following additional points should be noted. In *Rugiadose odorose*, where disagreements between the sources are given in footnotes, performers will need to consider the alternative readings. The two pieces by Durante, *Danza, danza, fanciulla* and *Vergin, tutt'amor*, were composed as vocal exercises – they can be performed as such, without words, and called 'Solfeggio'. In both songs the figuring is from the primary source, which uses 5̸ to indicate diminished 5ths rather than the more normal ♭5. Since a stroke through a figure usually indicates sharpening this has been altered here to ♭5, to avoid confusion. Finally, in the Rolli version of *Se tu m'ami*, which is discussed in the Preface, the first- and second-time bars are editorial, to allow different realizations for repeat and for continuation.

Michael Pilkington

Original key

Amarilli, mia bella

Solo madrigal

CACCINI

Original key signature has one flat.
* This line was altered to 'Dubitar non ti vale' (Doubting will not avail you) by Parisotti.

Original key: D

Vittoria, vittoria
'Amante sciolto d'Amore'
Canto

CARISSIMI

There is no key signature in the source; occasional missing accidentals have been supplied without comment. For dotted bar-lines, see 'Notes on this edition'.

* Some early editions give 'vil servitù' here and in bars 24, 32, 67 and 75, translated as 'love's vile desire'.

† Lower 8ve is for use with baritone.

Original key: C minor

Pietà, Signore
Preghiera

Attributed to STRADELLA

Andantino

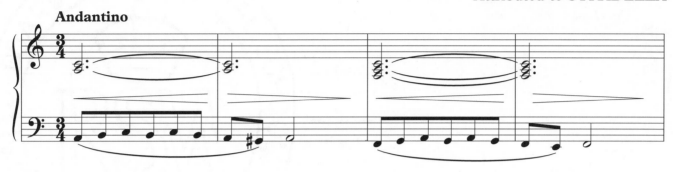

In the source the music is written out in full (without the *D.S. al Fine*). In this edition inconsistencies between the repeated sections have been reconciled without comment.

* In the source bars 54 and 64 both appear twice as the music is written out in full. *g'* is given as the top note of the first four chords in one bar but *a'* as the top note in the three other bars (in this transposition).

Original key: A minor

Che fiero costume
Aria

LEGRENZI

* Lower 8ve is for use with baritone.

Original key: A

Già il sole dal Gange

Aria from *L'honestà negli amori*

A. SCARLATTI

[Allegro ma non troppo]

RITORNELLO*

For dotted bar-lines, see 'Notes on this edition'.
*The transcription of the string ritornello shows what Scarlatti actually wrote (taking transposition into account).
† In the source, the viola has *c♯'* here and in bar 69, i.e. *g♯*, not *f♯*, in this transposition.

* Lower 8ve is for use with baritone.
† In the source, *A* here and in bar 93, i.e. *E*, not *F♯*, in this transposition.

★ *f♯* in the source, i.e. *c♯*, not *B*, in this transposition.

Original key: D minor

O cessate di piagarmi
Aria from *Il Pompeo*

A. SCARLATTI

The original aria was for male alto.

* Lower 8ve is for use with baritone.

* The transcription of the string ritornello shows what Scarlatti actually wrote (taking transposition into account).

Original key: A

Rugiadose odorose
'Le Violette'
Aria from *Il Pirro e Demetrio*

A. SCARLATTI

* Brackets denote unison violins.

* Lower 8ve is for use with baritone.
† ♪ ♪, not ♪ ♪, is given in Cullen and Walsh.

* Cullen and Walsh give the equivalent of *b*s for these four *c♯*'s, but see bars 19–21.

* Bracketed accidentals are from Cullen and Walsh.
† Cullen and Walsh give the equivalent of *g*♯; MS has equivalent of *f*♯.

Original key: C

Se Florinda è fedele

Aria from *La donna ancora è fedele*

A. SCARLATTI

* Brackets denote unison violins. For dotted bar-lines, see 'Notes on this edition'.

Pre-ghi, pian-ti e que-re-le io non a-scol - te - rò,
Plead-ing, weep-ing and com-plain-ing, I will not heed or care,

Ma se sa - rà fe - de - le, ma se sa - rà fe - de - le io m'in - na - mo - re -
But if she shows de - vo - tion, but if she shows de - vo - tion I'll know that she's my

- rò, io m'in - na - mo - re - rò, m'in - na - mo - re - rò, m'in - na - mo - re -
love, yes, know that she's my love. I shall fall in love, I shall fall in

- rò, io m'in - na - mo - re - rò. Se Flo - rin-da è fe - de - le io m'in - na -
love, yes, I___ shall___ fall___ in love. If Flo - rin-da is___ faith-ful then I shall

Original key: C minor

Spesso vibra per suo gioco

Aria from *La caduta de' Decemviri*

A. SCARLATTI

man - ca, que - sto man - ca_e quel vien me - no, que - sto
miss - es, this___ one miss - es, that one fades_ a - way, this___ one

man - ca, que - sto man - ca_e quel vien me - no.
miss - es, this___ one miss - es, that one fades_ a - way.

[p]

[f]

D.S. al Coda

⊕ CODA

Spes - so___
For___ a -

D.S. al Coda

⊕ CODA
RITORNELLO

Strs ff

Original key: F

Per la gloria d'adorarvi
Aria from *Griselda*

BONONCINI

Top line of piano follows unison violins of source 1.

Cue-sized trills appear in source 2 only.

Vocal underlay, slurring and beaming are from source 1.

Alternative underlay for bars 10–15 is from source 2, and would also apply to bars 18–23.

* Lower 8ve is for use with baritone.

Per la glo - ria d'a - do - rar - vi vo - glio_a -
Oh the pleas - ure and de - light of look - ing

- mar - vi_o lu - ci ca - re. A - man-do pe - ne - rò,
in - to your eyes, my dear. Well, I know I shall suf-fer,

Ma sem-pre v'a-me - rò, Sì, sì, nel mio pe - na -
But I will ev - er love you, Yes, yes, yes ev - er love

- re: A - man-do pe - ne - rò, Ma sem-pre v'a-me - rò,
you. Yes, I know I shall suf-fer, But I will ev - er love you,

Original key: G

Pur dicesti
Aria from *Arminio*

LOTTI (?)

* In this and all similar bars double dotting should be applied, to match the voice.

ca - ro sì, sì, Che fa— tut - to il mio pia - cer, il
sweet - est, 'yes', 'yes', I was— filled with love and hap - pi - ness, and

mio pia - cer. Pur di - ce - sti, ò
hap - pi - ness. When your— lips said (O

boc - ca, boc - ca bel - la, ò boc - ca, boc - ca bel - la, Quel so - a - ve e ca - ro—
lips, O lips so love - ly, O lips, O lips so love - ly) that so— dear and— sweet - est,—

sì, sì, quel so - a - ve e ca - ro sì, Che— fa tut - to il
'yes', 'yes', that so— dear and— sweet - est,— 'yes', I— was filled with love and

[*mf*]

[*p*]

[*mf cresc.*]

* Lower 8ve is for use with baritone.

Original key: G minor

Se tu m'ami

Canzonetta

Attributed to PERGOLESI

Andantino

mf

p cresc. *rit.*

Se tu m'a - mi, se tu so - spi - ri sol per me, gen - til pa -
If you love me, if you do sigh and pine for me, O shep - herd

p cresc.

p **a tempo**

-stor,_____ Ho do - lor de' tuoi mar - ti - ri, ho di - let - to
dear,_____ I am sor - ry for your suff - 'ring, I am hap - py

p

f **rit.**

del tuo a - mor,_____ Ma se pen - si che so - let - to io ti deb - ba ri -
in your lov - ing, But if I must love you on - ly, I'm a - fraid you are_____

f

AB 2730

Original key

Come raggio di sol
Canto

CALDARA

Co - me rag-gio di
Soft - ly the rays of

sol
sun,

mi - te_e se - re - no,
mild and se - rene - ly,

co - me rag - gio di
soft - ly the rays of

sol
sun,

mi - te_e se - re - no
mild and se - rene - ly

So - vra
Up - on

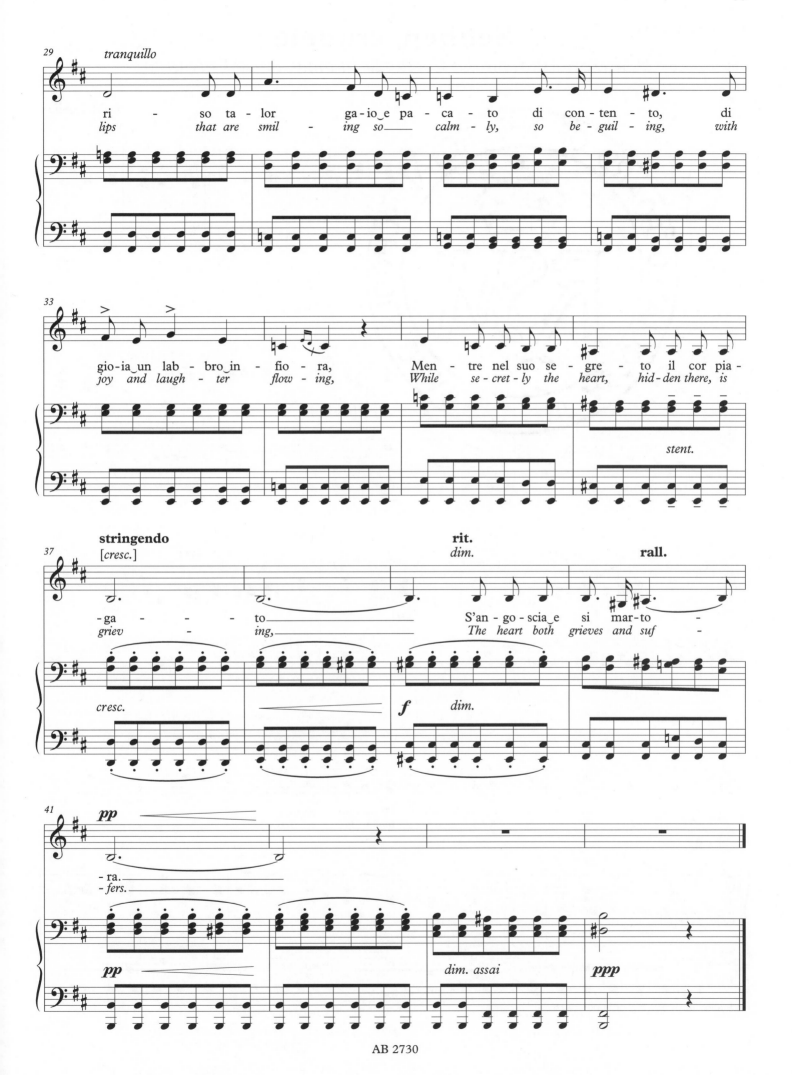

Original key: E minor

Sebben, crudele

Canzonetta from *La Costanza in amor vince l'inganno*

CALDARA

Seb - ben, cru - de - le,— mi fai— lan - guir,—
Though you are cru - el— and make— me suf - fer,

* Violins are an 8ve higher in the source.

Seb - ben, cru - de - le, mi fai lan - guir,___ Sem - pre fe - de - le ti
Though you are cru - el and make me suf - fer, I'm al - ways___ lov - ing you___

vo - glio_a - mar, sem - pre fe - de - le ti vo - glio_a - mar.
faith - ful - ly, I'm al - ways___ lov - ing you___ faith - ful - ly.

Original key: B minor

Vieni, vieni o mio diletto

Aria

VIVALDI

[Allegro]

Vns
colla voce

Vie - ni, vie - ni o mio di - let - to, ch'il mio co - re
Come, oh come thou fount of all my ec - sta - sy, al - rea-dy my heart,

tut - to af-fet - to già t'a - spet-ta e o-gnor ti chia - ma.
full of af-fec - tion, waits for you and it ev - er calls your name.

Vie - ni, vie - ni o mio di - let - to, ch'il mio co - re
Come, oh come thou fount of all my ec - sta-sy, al - rea-dy my heart,

tut - to af-fet - to già t'a - spet-ta e o-gnor ti chia - ma.
full of af-fec - tion, waits for you and it ev - er calls your name.

[cresc.]

Original key: C minor

Danza, danza, fanciulla
Arietta

DURANTE

The beaming in the vocal part follows source 2, though the music there is printed in 3/4 with double the number of bars.

Original key: D minor

Vergin, tutt'amor
Preghiera

DURANTE

*The gracenote *g'* should perhaps be *g♯'*, though it is not sharpened in either source.

65

AB 2730

Original key

Verdi prati
Aria from *Alcina*

HANDEL

Verdi prati selve a - me - ne,
Verdant pastures, forests pleasing,

per - de - re - te la bel - tà.
beauty will be lost so soon.

*The accompaniment is a transcription of Handel's string parts. The notes in small print indicate where the continuo would have completed the harmony.

Va - ghi fior cor - ren - ti ri - vi, la va -
Love - ly flow'rs, quick flow - ing stream - lets, the de -

- ghez - za, la bel - lez - za pre - sto in voi,_____ si
- sir - ing and the beau - ty will, in you,_____ so

can - ge - rà. Ver - di_____ pra - ti sel - ve a -
swift - ly fade. Ver - dant_____ pas - tures, for - ests

- me - ne, per - de - re - te la bel - tà,
pleas - ing, beau - ty_____ will be lost so soon,

per – – – –
beau – – – –

per – de – re – te la bel – tà,
beau – ty will be lost so soon,

per – de – re – te la bel – tà.
beau – ty will be lost so soon.

Cont.

Strs f

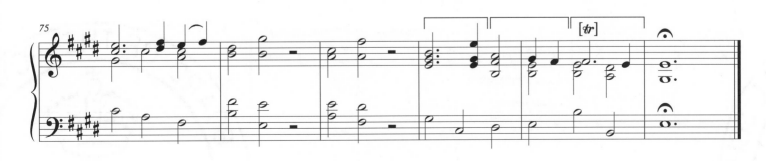

Original key: D

Se tu m'ami
Canzonetta

ROLLI (?)

Original key: A

Chi vuol la Zingarella?

Cavatina

PAISIELLO

[Allegretto]

Vns & cont.

p

[in free time]

[colla voce]

Ahi lo trep-pie-de e lo spie-do, ahi lo trep-pie-de e lo
I stand cook-ing by a caul-dron, I stand cook-ing by a

spie-do. Chi vuol la Zin-ga-rel-la? Gra-zio-sa ac-cor-da e bel-la, Si-
caul-dron. Who wants the lit-tle gyp-sy? I'm grace-ful, quick and clev-er, Well,_

-gno-ri ec-co la____ qua, Si-gno-ri ec-co la qua.
gen-tle-men, I'm____ here, well, gen-tle-men, I'm here.

vuol la Zin - ga - rel - la? Gra - zio - sa_ac - cor - da_e bel - la, Si -
wants the lit - tle gyp - sy? *I'm grace - ful, quick and clev - er,* *Well,—*

-gno - ri_ec - co la— qua, Si - gno - ri_ec - co la— qua.
gen - tle - men, I'm— here, *well, gen - tle - men, I'm— here.*

Le don - ne sul bal - co - ne So be - ne_in - do - vi - nar;
The wo - men on the bal - co - ny, *Their for - tune I can tell,*

I gio - va - ni_al can - to - ne So me - glio stuz - zi - car. A -
The young men on the pro - me - nade, *I tease them all the time.* *In -*

Source notes

BONONCINI **Per la gloria d'adorarvi**

Ernesto's aria from *Griselda*. Libretto by Paolo Antonio Rolli (1687–1765) after Apostolo Zeno (1668–1750). First performed at the King's Theatre, London, 22 February 1722. Sources: 1. Score published by J. Walsh & Son and Joseph Hare, London, 1722. British Library, London (H.321.b.). 2. ''Tis my Glory to adore you. A favourite song in *Griselda* in English and Italian', published anonymously, London, 1722. British Library, London (H.1601.(460.)).

CACCINI **Amarilli, mia bella**

Words by Alessandro or Giovanni Battista Guarini. Sources: 1. 'Le nuove Musiche', published by I. Marescotti, Florence, 1601 (1602). Biblioteca Nazionale Centrale, Florence (M.A.31.III). 2. 'Le nuove Musiche', published by Alessandro Rauerii, Venice, 1602 (1607). British Library, London (K.8.h.14.).

CALDARA **Come raggio di sol**

There being no early source, authenticity cannot be guaranteed. Source: 19th-century MS, Österreichische Nationalbibliothek, Vienna (S.M.23258).

CALDARA **Sebben, crudele**

From dramma pastorale *La Costanza in amor vince l'inganno*, Act I, Scene 3. Librettist unidentified. First performed at Palazzo Bonelli, Rome, 9 February 1711. Source: MS score dated 1711. Biblioteca Musicale di Conservatorio di Musica 'S. Cecilia', Rome (G.Ms.184).

CARISSIMI **Vittoria, vittoria** ('Amante sciolto d'Amore')

Words by Domenico Benigni (1596–1653). Source: MS score. Biblioteca Estense, Modena (Ms.Mus.G.28).

DURANTE **Danza, danza, fanciulla**

This and the following aria were conceived as solfeggi or vocal exercises, and published in various editions of *Solfèges d'Italie* in Paris, including 1772, 1786 and *c*.1812. It is not known when words were added, though it was before 1870. Sources: 1. No. 132 from *Solfèges d'Italie, avec la Basse chiffrée*, 2nd edition, collected by Levesque and Bêche, and published by Sr. Cousineau, Paris, *c*.1780. Royal College of Music, London (26.B.13). 2. The text follows that given in *Echos d'Italie*, Vol. 6 (*Les maitres italiens*), published by Durand & Schoenewerk, Paris, a reprint of that published by G. Flaxland, ?1860.

DURANTE **Vergin, tutt'amor**

See *Danza, danza, fanciulla* above. Sources: 1. No. 146 from the same collection. 2. As for *Danza, danza, fanciulla*.

HANDEL **Verdi prati**

Ruggiero's aria from *Alcina*, Act II, Scene 2. Libretto by Antonio Marchi (*fl.* 1692–1725) adapted from *L'isola di Alcina*, 1728, after Ludovico Ariosto's *Orlando furioso*. First performed at Theatre Royal, Covent Garden, London, 16 April 1735. Source: Autograph MS score, dated 8 April 1735. British Library, London (Add.MS 31566).

LEGRENZI **Che fiero costume**

Source: From a cantata in *Echi di riverenza*, Op. 14, published by Giocomo Monti, Bologna, 1678. Civico Museo Bibliografico Musicale, Bologna. Photo-reproduction in *Archivum Musicum*, Vol. 7 (Firenze: Studio per Edizioni Scelte, 1980) and *The Italian Cantata*, Vol. 6 (New York: Garland, 1986).

LOTTI (?) **Pur dicesti**

From *Arminio*. The authorship of this opera is unknown, though this aria has frequently been published under Lotti's name. Another aria from the opera has been ascribed to Alessandro Scarlatti in a MS in the Fitzwilliam Museum, Cambridge. Source: Score of 'Songs in the Opera of Arminius, as they are Perform'd at the Queens Theatre', published by J. Walsh and J. Hare, London, 1714. British Library, London (H.322).

PAISIELLO **Chi vuol la Zingarella?**

Source: MS score, Biblioteca Casanatense, Rome (Ms.2521).

PERGOLESI, attrib. **Se tu m'ami**

Words by Paolo Antonio Rolli (1687–1765). Although this canzonetta bears some similarity to Pergolesi's aria 'Ogni pena più spietata' in his opera *Lo frate 'nnamorato* of 1732, no known MS exists and this attribution is, as yet, unauthenticated. It has been suggested that this song, which appeared in Alessandro Parisotti's *Arie Antiche* in 1885, is most probably a 19th-century forgery. Sources: 1. *Arie Antiche*, Vol. 1, edited by Alessandro Parisotti, published by Ricordi, Milan, 1885. 2. *Opera Omnia di Giov. Batt. Pergolesi*, Vol. 22 (*Canzone con accomp. di quartetto d'archi*), published by Gli amici della musica da camera, Roma, 1939–43. British Library, London (F.1110.a.). This is a copy of Parisotti's song.

ROLLI (?) **Se tu m'ami**

This comes from *Di Canzonette e di Cantate Libri Due*. The texts are by Paolo Antonio Rolli, who, since no other composer is indicated, may also have provided the music. Published by Thomas Edlin, London, 1727. British Library, London (1062.l.28.).

A. SCARLATTI **Già il sole dal Gange**

Saldino's aria from the opera *L'honestà negli amori*, Act III, Scene 10. Libretto by D. F. Bernini (or Domenico Filippo Contini (*fl.* 1669–87), according to D'Accone 1985). First performed at Palace of Queen Christina, Rome, 3 February 1680. Source: Undated MS score, Biblioteca Estense, Modena (Mus.F.1057).

A. SCARLATTI **O cessate di piagarmi**

Sesto's aria from the opera *Il Pompeo*, Act II, Scene 5. Libretto by Count Nicolò Minato (*c.*1630–98). First performed at Teatro Colonna, Rome, 25 January 1683. Source: Bibliothèque Royale Albert Ier, Brussels, MS II 3962 (Fétis 2519). Photo-reproduction in *Handel Sources*, Vol. 6 (New York: Garland, 1986).

A. SCARLATTI **Rugiadose odorose** ('Le Violette')

Mario's aria from the opera *Il Pirro e Demetrio*. Libretto by Adriano Morselli (*fl.* 1676–91). First performed at Teatro San Bartolomeo, Naples, 28 January 1694. Sources: 1. MS score, Biblioteca del Conservatorio di Musica 'S. Pietro a Majella', Naples. 2. 'Songs in the New Opera of Pyrrhus and Demetrius' (with additions by N. F. Haym), printed by T. Cross Jnr and published by John Cullen, London, 1709. British Library, London (I.355). 3. 'Songs in the New Opera call'd Pyrrhus and Demetrius' (with additions by N. F. Haym), published by J. Walsh, P. Randall and J. Hare, London, 1709. British Library, London (H.109).

A. SCARLATTI **Se Florinda è fedele**

Alidoro's aria from the opera *La donna ancora è fedele*. Libretto after Domenico Filippo Contini (*fl.* 1669–87). First performed at Teatro San Bartolomeo, Naples, autumn 1698. Source: MS score, Biblioteca del Conservatorio di Musica 'S. Pietro a Majella', Naples (49a.2.3).

A. SCARLATTI **Spesso vibra per suo gioco**

Claudia's aria from the opera *La caduta de' Decemviri*, Act I, Scene 15. Libretto by Silvio Stampiglia (1664–1725). First performed at Teatro San Bartolomeo, Naples, 15 December 1697. Source: 18th-century MS score, British Library, London (Add.MS.14170).

STRADELLA, attrib. **Pietà, Signore**

The sources are 18th century and authenticity cannot be guaranteed. *The New Grove Dictionary of Music and Musicians*, 2nd edn, states that this aria 'is not by Stradella, although it bears his name on hundreds of copies and arrangements; it was possibly composed as a spoof by F.-J. Fétis, although it has also been attributed to Louis Niedermeyer'. Source: MS transcription by Pietro Canal, Biblioteca Nazionale Marciana, Venice (Ms.It.IV.1776(11322)).

VIVALDI **Vieni, vieni o mio diletto**

This aria was possibly intended for inclusion in one of Vivaldi's early operas (perhaps *Ottone in villa*). Source: Autograph MS score, Biblioteca Nazionale Universitaria, Turin (Foà 28, f.102).

Printed in England by Caligraving Ltd, Thetford, Norfolk